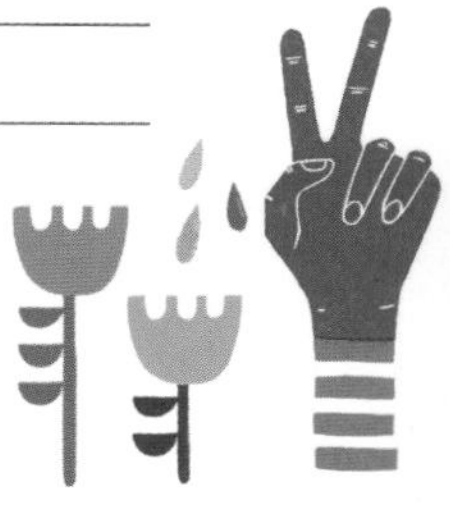

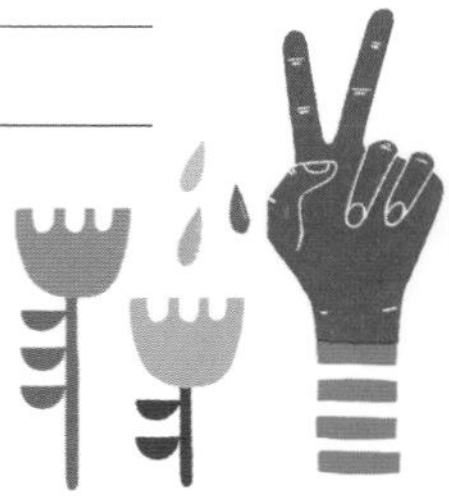

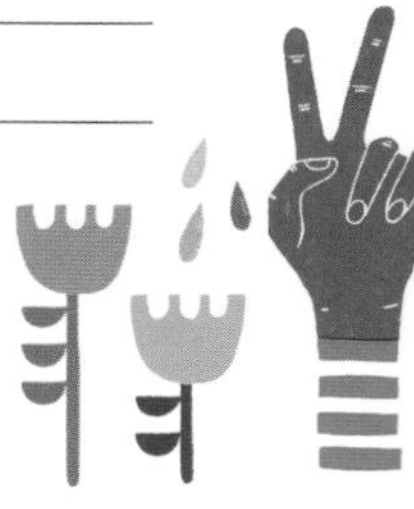

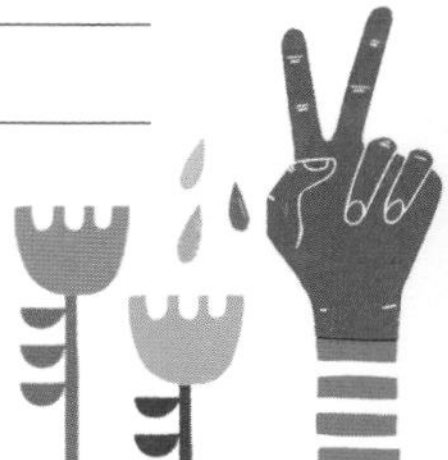

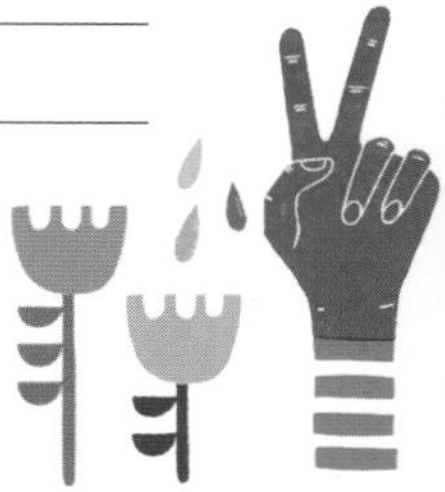

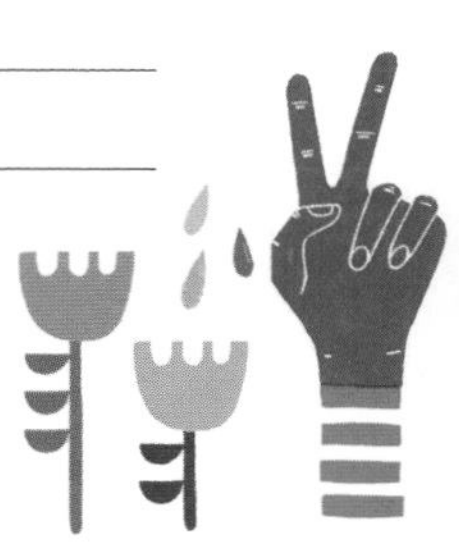

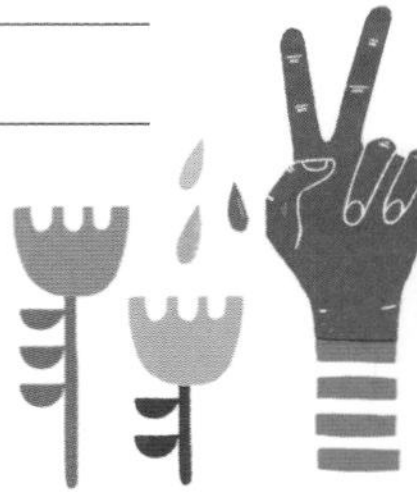

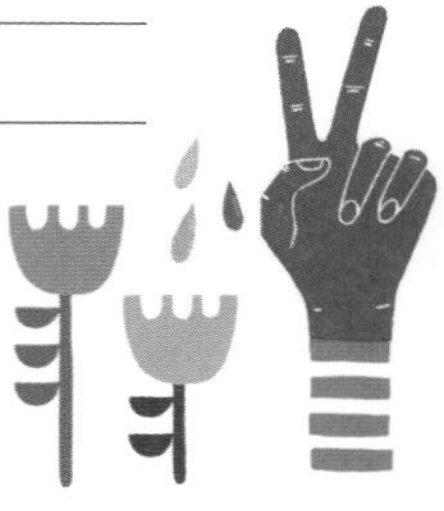

Who's There™
Illustrations © Lisa Congdon

6080 Center Drive, Los Angeles, CA 90045
Made in China / Fabriqué en Chine / Hecho en China